John Thompson's
MELODY ALL THE WAY!

PIANO TUITION
ON A TUNEFUL BASIS

GRADE I

WILLIS MUSIC COMPANY
Cincinnati

© 1949 & 1963 The Willis Music Co.

Exclusive distributors:
Music Sales Limited, 8/9 Frith Street, London W1V 5TZ.
Music Sales Pty Limited, 120 Rothschild Avenue, Rosebery, NSW 2018, Australia

FOREWORD

The MELODY ALL THE WAY series is published in response to the insistent plea of countless piano teachers who fully subscribe to the author's standards of teaching material and teaching ideas, but who find themselves in a quandary when two children are studying in the same family, or where neighbouring children "start" together. The heartaches that naturally arise if one child progresses somewhat faster than the other are obviated if the youngsters are not using identical books.

The MELODY ALL THE WAY series is planned not to *supplant* the MODERN COURSE FOR THE PIANO, but as *interchangeable* with that work. Some teachers find it sound practice to use two study books simultaneously—one, of course, serving the purpose of a supplementary book for sight-reading and additional practice material. Grade 1 of MELODY ALL THE WAY would be ideal for this use in connection with the *first half* of "The First Grade Book" from THE MODERN COURSE FOR THE PIANO.

It should be observed that each Course is complete in itself, permitting individual or interchangeable use.

FAMILIAR AIRS

In so far as possible, the musical examples in MELODY ALL THE WAY have been adapted from familiar airs —folk tunes, themes from symphonies, well-known piano solos, songs, etc. This has an advantage for the young student: getting away from cut-and-dried text, and giving him the thrill of performing, in simplified versions, music which he hears frequently on the radio, gramophone records, etc.

FIVE-FINGER POSITION

The first examples in this book are in simple five-finger position. New positions are learned as new KEYS are introduced. Later on, *two* positions are combined in a piece.

Still later, by passing under the thumb, the pupil is taught to move smoothly from one position to the other. Thus the way is prepared for scale playing. Many examples, it will be noted, appear with accompanying Preparatory Studies. Benefits of this procedure will be obvious at once to the experienced teacher.

PLAYING WITH EXPRESSION

There is no sound reason why the elementary pianist should not be required to play with *musical expression* and *understanding*. The simplest melody can be interesting if played with definite intention. Real interpretation consists of more than simply following the marks of dynamics. It includes *colour*—the result of employing various Touches.

Even a beginner can master the Touches. Taught in their fundamental form, they offer no real problem, and the result in stimulating real musicianship will richly reward the efforts of teacher and pupil alike.

HANON PRELIMINARY EXERCISES—FOR DEVELOPING THE TOUCHES

John Thompson's edition of the Hanon Preliminary Exercises is carefully designed to develop these fundamental touches. The studies are arranged in Crotchets, and each page is attractively illustrated and titled.

The Phrasing Touch, Finger Legato, Finger Staccato, Wrist Staccato, Forearm Staccato and Legato, Portamento, Rotary Motion, etc., are treated in consecutive order.

To accomplish *maximum* results Hanon's Preliminary Exercises should be introduced when the pupil reaches page 14 of this book. Improvement in interpretation will be apparent almost immediately.

TEMPO

While each example bears a Tempo indication—*Moderato, Andante, Allegro*, etc., the *actual* rate of speed should be decided by the teacher, since pupils vary so widely in ability. While encouraging an increased tempo in review work, the wise teacher never allows speed to go beyond the point of *precision*—always a most important objective.

FIRST GRADE STUDIES

For *general* technical work the author's FIRST GRADE STUDIES are especially designed for pupils at the present level. They may be used, at the discretion of the teacher, either *toward the end* of Grade 1 or *at the beginning* of Grade 1-Plus.

The author has kept in mind the fact that all examples, even technical exercises, must be tuneful if the young pupil's interest is to be retained.

Properly used, the FIRST GRADE STUDIES become at once a means of developing *independence, strength, evenness* and *speed* of finger action, together with *reading* and *expression*.

MUSIC WRITING BOOKS

(For home work)

Every teacher appreciates the value of Music Writing Books for home work.

The author has designed three such Writing Books for the elementary pianist. The time of their assignment is a matter of individual preference on the part of the teacher but they should be used in the following order: THE NOTE SPELLER, THE SCALE SPELLER and THE CHORD SPELLER.

CERTIFICATE OF MERIT

A Certificate of Merit has been included on page 45 as recognition of the successful completion of this book. It should be signed and dated by the teacher.

CONTENTS

CHRISTMAS CAROLS

6

HAND POSITION

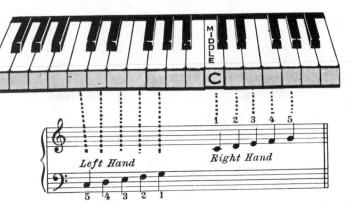

Left Hand   *Right Hand*
5 4 3 2 1   1 2 3 4 5

The New York Philharmonic-Symphony Orchestra

Place the hands in the position shown above, then play the following
Finger Drill.

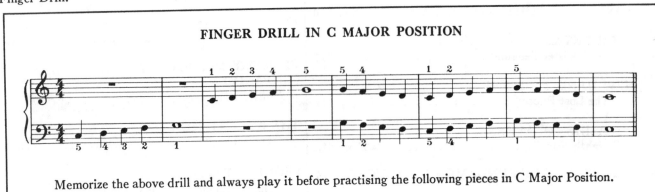

FINGER DRILL IN C MAJOR POSITION

Memorize the above drill and always play it before practising the following pieces in C Major Position.

Listen for this theme when the 9th
Symphony is played on your radio.

Theme from

Symphony No. 9

1st Phrase

Beethoven

2nd Phrase

MUSIC, like language, is divided into sentences.   A musical sentence is called a PHRASE.

Note how one phrase answers the other in the above example.

W. M. Co. 6602
(46346)

Made in England

Before playing this piece, *always* play the Finger Drill in C major Position as shown on page 6.

THE TIE

The TIE is a curved line joining together two notes *of the same pitch* and indicates that the second note is held for its full value *without being played.*

Cradle Song

from Schubert

Sleep thou, sleep thou,

Moth - er's arms en - fold Thee,

Rest thou, rest_____ thou,

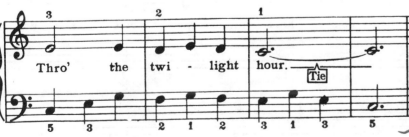

Thro' the twi - light hour. Tie

RHYTHM AND ACCENTS

The life of any composition depends upon its rhythmical "swing". The first and most important step in establishing Rhythm is ACCENT.

In THREE-FOUR rhythm always accent the first beat of each bar.

W.M.Co. 6602

TONAL SHADING

A skilful painter adds charm to a picture by careful blending of colours. It is a well established rule that "Contrast is the first Law of all Art".

One way of getting contrast in music is by means of Tonal Shading—loud and soft; moderately loud and moderately soft, etc.

Read the definitions at the bottom of the next page and apply the various tonal effects indicated in the following piece.

Even a simple first-grade piece can be very effective if played with CONTRAST.

A good rule to remember in all playing is that "A MELODY LINE IS CONSTANTLY CHANGING ITS THICKNESS"—from loud to soft and vice versa.

The Child and the Bobolink

Moderato - *legato*

mf Bob - o - link, Bob - o - link, fly to me, fly to me,

Don't stay so high in the Wil - - low,

p I would make room for you here in my crib, If you

on - ly would hop on my pil - - low.

* *BOBOLINK:* American bird named for its call. It is the size of a starling but looks more like a sparrow.

THE MEANING OF THE EXPRESSION MARKS USED IN THIS PIECE

—Read Carefully—

MODERATO—*At a moderate rate of speed or tempo.*
LEGATO—*Bound together, play smoothly and connected.*
mf = Mezzo-forte. *Half or moderately loud.*
p = Piano. *Softly.*
f = Forte. *Loud.*
pp = Pianissimo. *Very soft.*
mp = Mezzo-piano. *Half or moderately soft.*
Rit. = Ritard. *Gradual slowing up of tempo.*

SEMITONES AND TONES

A SEMITONE is the distance between any key and the next nearest key—up or down. There will be no key—white or black—lying in between.

A TONE is twice as big as a semitone. Therefore there will always be ONE KEY— either white or black—lying between.

Semitone

C D E

Tone

From C to the black key on the right is a SEMITONE. There is no key in between.

From C to D is a TONE. There is one key (black) lying in between.

Most semitones are found between a white key and a black key. There are however, two WHITE SEMITONES—one between E and F and the other between B and C.

WHITE SEMITONES

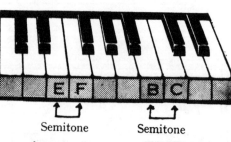

Semitone   Semitone

SHARPS AND FLATS

A SHARP (♯) placed before a note RAISES it a semitone.

A FLAT (♭) placed before a note LOWERS it a semitone.

It will be seen therefore that each black key has two names—one as a SHARP and the other as a FLAT.

On the charts below write in both the SHARP and FLAT names of each black key.

SHARP NAMES

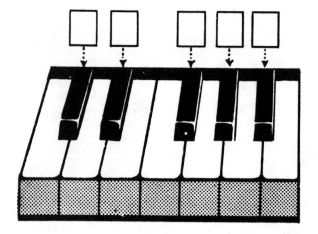

FLAT NAMES

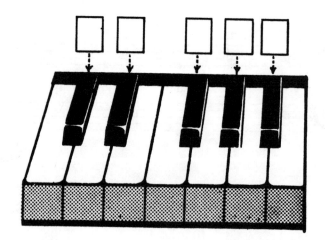

THE NATURAL

A NATURAL (♮) placed before a note cancels the sharp or flat previously in effect.

ACCIDENTALS

New Hand Position

Poor Mr. Penguin

Moderato

Look at Mis-ter Pen-guin, In his din-ner clothes,

He just has to wear them ev-'ry sin-gle place he goes.

I can wear my old clothes when I want to play,

But for Mis-ter Pen-guin it is Sun-day ev-'ry day!

In the following exercises write T for Tones and S for Semitones.

S

T

NEW HAND POSITION (G MAJOR)

FINGER DRILL IN G MAJOR POSITION

The Lost Puppy

Moderato

Oh where, oh where can my lit-tle dog be? And oh why, oh

why has he wan-dered from me? I pam-pered and led him, I

wa-tered and fed him, Oh where, oh where can that naugh-ty dog be?

TEMPO

Count evenly so as to preserve a steady Tempo.
Always review the pieces already learned and try to increase the Tempo when musically
justified.

PHRASING

Phrasing in music is indicated by curved lines called SLURS.

All notes under the slur sign must be smoothly connected. The last note of the slur however, is tossed off and thus held for somewhat less time than its actual value.

LEFT HAND POSITION
With one-note extension.

Lightly Row

QUAVERS
There are two QUAVERS to one count.

See page 44 *for explanation of all musical terms used in this book.*

NOTE TO TEACHERS

At this point the young pupil should be assigned the John Thompson edition of **Hanon-Preliminary Exercises.** This edition is designed to promote the agility, independence, strength and perfect evenness of fingers which constitute the original objectives of **Hanon,** and to develop simultaneously the various *fundamental touches* used in playing the piano with expression.

It has long been the contention of the Author that young pianists should be taught to use in *miniature* the same pianistic attacks used by concert artists. This point needs no discussion since its value has been proved over a period of years.

The book begins with the **Phrasing Touch** (presented on the preceding page) and follows with **Finger Legato, Finger Staccato, Wrist Staccato, Forearm Staccato, Portamento Playing, Rotary Motion,** etc.—all treated in consecutive order with illustrations, titles and complete explanatory text. Its study gives the young pianist an appreciation of the uses of the fundamental touches so that they can be applied readily to First and Second Grade pieces. The improved tone quality will be found a stimulus to Interpretation in these early grades. Sample pages of the book are shown below.

HANON PRELIMINARY EXERCISES

A First Grade edition—in crotchets—of this standard work for the piano.
It has been especially designed to develop *fundamental* touches in piano playing.
Titled and illustrated for added interest.

TWO-NOTE AND THREE-NOTE PHRASING

The Prince and Princess

Observe the Phrasing marks

Play with as much expression as possible and note the new **Expression Signs.**

means **Crescendo**, *a gradual increase in tone.*

means **Decrescendo**, *a gradual decrease in tone.*

Don't overlook the two-note and three-note slurs (phrasing signs) shown by the little curved lines over certain notes.

Suggestion for supplementary solo in sheet form

THE DUTCH TWINS by Willa Ward is a humorous dance which develops two-note phrasing and tonal contrast.

W.M.Co. 6602

SCALES

THE matter of Scales and Arpeggio practice is a much debated question among piano teachers. Some teachers begin scale work quite early in the pupil's career and are very insistent in the matter of daily practice. Others look upon them as a sort of unnecessary drudgery and claim that pupils can develop just as much facility in playing the scale and arpeggio passages that occur in the books and sheet music of their repertoire. Naturally, this resolves itself into a matter of individual judgment.

THE author feels that since all music is made up of scales and arpeggio figures, or fragments thereof, pupils should be required to know something about them. All music has form and shape that should be recognized in order to aid interpretation and general musicianship. There is also a technical value to scales and arpeggio practice which cannot be summarily dismissed. Perhaps the real difficulty arises from the theory that most pupils look upon the scale as a dry, uninteresting exercise invented by the teacher as a special form of punishment. If more care were used in presenting the scale and a real effort made to have the pupil look upon the scale as a beautiful piece of musical architecture, the result would be quite different. As soon as the formation of a scale is learned, pupils should be assigned pieces in which the scale figure is employed as melody. In this way the pupil learns to greet the scale as an *interesting musical pattern*—and one which will recur many times even in elementary repertoire.

THERE are many ways to teach the scales. But most of the variations are based upon two standard approaches. Some teachers prefer the *tetrachord* approach while others find the older formula (i.e., the semitones between the third and fourth and the seventh and eighth) more acceptable. Of course, this is a matter that will vary not only with teachers but with pupils. This book has been arranged so that either approach may be made at the discretion of the teacher.

JOHN THOMPSON'S "SCALE SPELLER"

To assure mastery of Scale Construction, John Thompson's SCALE SPELLER should be introduced at this point. It is a Writing Book designed for Home Work and teaches the pupil all INTERVALS, MAJOR and MINOR SCALES, KEY SIGNATURES, etc.

THE MAJOR SCALE

A SCALE is a succession of eight notes bearing letter-names in alphabetical order, the last note having the same letter-name as the first. The figures 1, 2, 3, 4, 5, 6, 7, 8 are called the degrees of the scale.

A MAJOR SCALE is a succession of WHOLE tones and semitones.
The semitones occur between 3 and 4 and between 7 and 8 as follows:

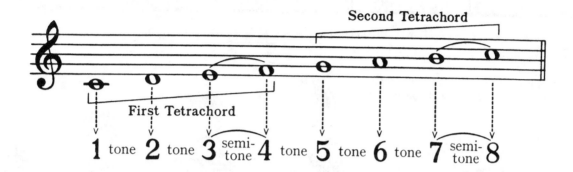

The above chart shows how a MAJOR SCALE is composed of TWO TETRACHORDS, each tetrachord *separated by a WHOLE tone.*

Play the scale of C MAJOR as follows, using the fingers indicated.

SCALE OF G MAJOR

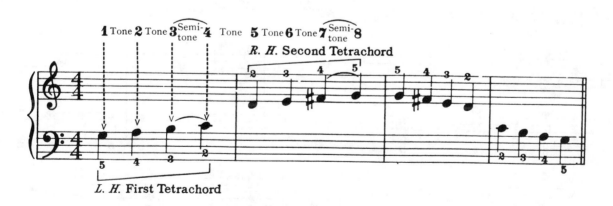

Note to Teachers: *During the progress in this book, it is advisable to adhere to the above form—the scale divided between the hands—until scale construction in all keys has been thoroughly mastered. This obviates the necessity of passing the thumb under and the hand over—a procedure which is comprehensively taken up and illustrated by examples in later books.*

W. M. Co. 6602

SCALE OF C MAJOR—*Ascending*

Upper Tetrachord
Right hand

Lower Tetrachord
Left hand

Marching, marching all together side by side.
Learning like the big Scouts how to keep in
    stride.
Marching, marching all together,
Staunch in fair or stormy weather,
Every pack of Cubs shares friendship true and
    tried.

March of the Cubs

Allegro

See page 44 for definitions of all terms and signs used in this book.

SCALE OF G MAJOR—*Descending*

THE melody used in this piece has an interesting history. It was originally an old Scottish Folk-Tune, sung by the herders while tending their flocks of sheep. It has also been crooned as a Lullaby around many a Scottish hearth. Its beauty and simplicity so impressed the great German musician, Brahms, that he composed in 1892 an Intermezzo for piano using this air as the principal theme.

The adaptation here presented lies in the five-finger position and is an excellent example of the *scale used as melody*. Brahms and many other great masters recognized the scale as a beautiful bit of musical structure, and in this particular piece the simple descending major scale fashions a lullaby beloved by all the world. It is often used as a Christmas carol for which reason it makes an interesting addition to the Yuletide concert programme.

Lullaby

adapted from
Johannes Brahms

See page **44** *for musical definitions.*

CHORD BUILDING
Intervals

An INTERVAL is the difference in pitch between 2 notes.

INTERVALS are measured by the number of LETTER NAMES contained between the LOWER and UPPER notes *inclusively*.

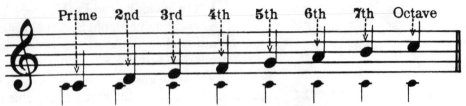

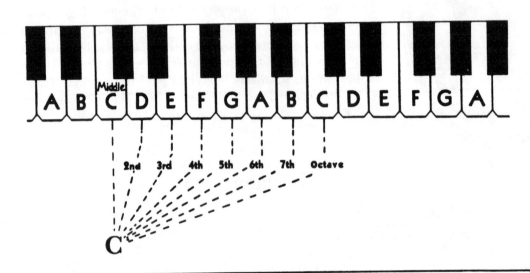

TRIADS

A CHORD is a group of THREE or more notes

All SCALES are built in steps of 2nd's.   For instance : *C to D, D to E: E-F etc.*

All CHORDS are built in steps of 3rd's.   "   "   : *C to E: E to G: G-B etc.*

The NOTE on which a CHORD is built is called the ROOT.

A TRIAD is a chord of THREE notes and contains a ROOT, a 3rd and a 5th.

EVERY CHORD IS NAMED FOR ITS ROOT

If we take the FIRST, THIRD and FIFTH notes of the Scale of C major

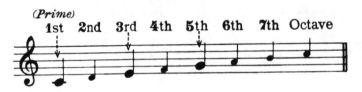

And sound them to-gether thus:

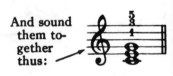

we have played the **C MAJOR TRIAD**

G is the 5th
E is the 3rd
C is the ROOT

When the C major TRIAD or any Chord is played in the following manner:

it is called a BROKEN CHORD or ARPEGGIO.

CHORD INVERSIONS

We have learned that a TRIAD contains a ROOT, a 3rd and a 5th. The order of these notes may change *without changing the name of the chord.*

When the lowest note is the ROOT, the triad is in the ROOT POSITION.
When the lowest note is NOT the ROOT, the triad is said to be INVERTED.

C MAJOR TRIAD

Example:

Root Position
Note Root at bottom

First Inversion
Root in first place on top

Second Inversion
Root in second place

Simple rules for recognizing INVERTED CHORDS
TRIADS are in the ROOT POSITION when all the intervals of the Chord look alike; that is, when the notes are either ALL on the LINES or ALL in the SPACES.

Example: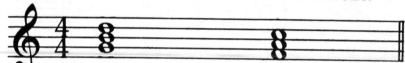

All the notes are LINE notes, therefore the TRIAD is in the ROOT position. G is the root

All the notes are in the SPACES therefore the TRIAD is in the ROOT position. F is the root.

When TRIADS are INVERTED the intervals of the chord are unalike—appear mixed: that is, some of the notes are on the LINES and some are in SPACES.

C MAJOR TRIAD

Example: No. 1

Root Position
All the notes are line notes

First Inversion
Two line notes and one space note

Second Inversion
One line note and two space notes

F MAJOR TRIAD

Example: No. 2

Root Position
All the notes are space notes

First Inversion
Two space notes and one line note

Second Inversion
One space note and two line notes

The ROOT is always the FIRST NOTE (counting upwards) to change its position from SPACE to LINE or from LINE to SPACE.

W.M.Co.6602

BROKEN CHORDS
PREPARATORY STUDY

Over the Waves

Moderato

Suggestion for supplementary solo in sheet form

FOREST DAWN in C major by John Thompson, will prove an exemplary recital **piece** to facilitate **BROKEN CHORD** playing.

W.M.Co. 6602

NEW KEY—F MAJOR

New Hand Position

The Key of F Major—
has one flat—B♭

Over the Fence is Out !

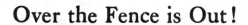

Animato

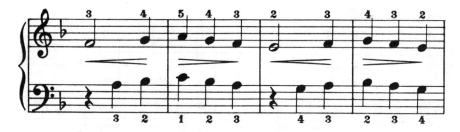

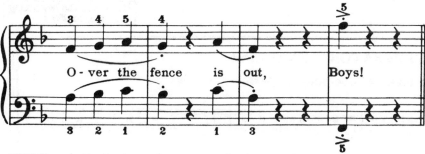

O - ver the fence is out, Boys!

W.M.Co. 6602

CHANGING HAND POSITIONS

To play this piece the right hand is required to move from one hand position to another.
Practise making this change until you can do it smoothly then proceed with the piece.

1st Position—*R.H.*

2nd Position—*R.H.*

The Old Grey Goose

Folk Tune

Moderato

mp Go tell Aunt Nan - cy, Go tell Aunt Nan - cy

Fine

mf Go tell Aunt Nan - cy, The Old Grey Goose is dead.

Change Hand Position

Now she'll be co - sy in the win - ter

poco rit.

pp Down for her pil - low and her bed.

Da Capo al Fine

Return to the beginning
and play to *Fine*

PREPARATORY EXERCISE

First each hand separately then together one octave apart.

R.H.

L.H.

CHANGING HAND POSITIONS

Hand Position

PREPARATORY EXERCISE

Each hand separately then together one octave apart

Evening Song

Moderato

German Folk Tune

Float, float, soft lit - tle cloud - let, Glow,

moon, o - ver the trees. Shine, sun,

shine on the mor - row, Bring-ing a soft sum-mer breeze.

Change Hand Position

mf

Change Hand Position   *mp*

Play the Scale of F Major before playing this piece.

Also the Broken Chord divided between the hands, in the same form as the Preparatory Exercise on page 22.

W.M.Co.6602

CHANGING HAND POSITIONS
In this piece the right hand plays in three different Hand Positions

At the Carnival

Moderato

Play left hand staccato throughout

Change Hand Position

mf

Change Hand Position

Change Hand Position

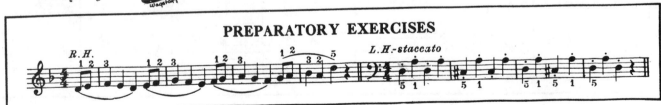

PREPARATORY EXERCISES

R.H.

L.H.-staccato

Suggestion for supplementary solo in sheet form

MOCCASIN DANCE by Lois Long is an excellent recital number to assign at this point.

W.M.Co. 6602

CHANGING HAND POSITIONS

The Judge's Dance

from
Swedish Folk Song

PREPARATORY EXERCISES

FIRST CONCERT PIECE
PREPARATORY EXERCISE

This is your first concert piece. Note that the right hand is required to play in both Treble and Bass Clefs. Memorize it and be sure to observe all expression marks.

Through the Woods

from
French Folk Song

Andante moderato

Right hand over

poco rit.

mp a tempo

p

pp

DOTTED CROTCHETS

You have already played *dotted minims* and learned how the DOT set after a note increases the time of that note by half its value. Therefore, if a CROTCHET is equal to ONE count, a dotted crotchet will naturally be equal to ONE COUNT and A HALF,—or one full beat and half of the next one.

Introduction of the *dotted crotchet* adds a new RHYTHMICAL PATTERN to those already learned.

PREPARATORY EXERCISE

Melody Pattern   Same figure using the Tie   Same effect using the
                                                                        dot instead of the Tie.

Largo
adapted from "New World" Symphony

Antonin Dvořák

Slowly with much expression

Antonin Dvořák (1841-1904) was active nearer our own day than most of the great masters. Dvořák loved the Folk Tunes of his native Bohemia. He was very close to the peasant folk of the lands he visited. When he went to America in 1892 he was fascinated by the Negro Spirituals and Folk Tunes of that country and used them as a basis for themes in his great symphony, "From the New World".

The Air here given is from the Largo (second movement) of the New World Symphony and is frequently heard on the radio.

Listen for this theme next time it is being played by orchestra.

Suggestion for supplementary solo in sheet form
SWAYING SILVER BIRCHES by Charles Leslie is an ideal teaching piece.

W.M.Co.6602

ROBERT SCHUMANN

1810–1856

Robert Schumann was a "romantic" composer. There were a number of these musicians who lived in the nineteenth century. Many of the critics of his day did not like the new "romantic" school of music to which Schumann belonged and one of them said that when Schumann was composing he liked to "dream with the pedal down."

Schumann liked children and had five sons and three daughters of his own. He wrote a series of pieces called "Album for the Young" and another called "Scenes from Childhood". His wife, Clara Schumann, who was a very noted pianist, helped to make his music famous.

The composer who loved children.

> *Play the left hand chords with a light touch so as not to interfere with the graceful flow of the melody.*

from
Little Romance

ACCENTS

Apply special stress (*accent*) to all notes or chords marked thus,

Tulip Time

(Dutch Dance)

GEORGE FRIDERIC HANDEL
1685–1759

Surprised at Practice.

When George Frideric was born his father said, "This baby shall some day be a great lawyer!" But as the little fellow grew up in the town of Halle, Germany, he cared for nothing in the world but music. He found an old clavichord in an unused attic and on this he practised as often as he could. When Handel was seven years old his father discovered him playing the old clavichord and was furious with him! Later his friends persuaded the father that young George Frideric would make a poor lawyer but a very good musician, and the father allowed the talented boy to study music. When Handel grew up he made England his home and became very famous. Perhaps you have heard the beautiful music of his best loved work, "The Messiah", on the radio or at church.

The charm of this piece lies in the sudden changes from forte to pianissimo. Be sure to observe them exactly as written.

from
The Harmonious Blacksmith

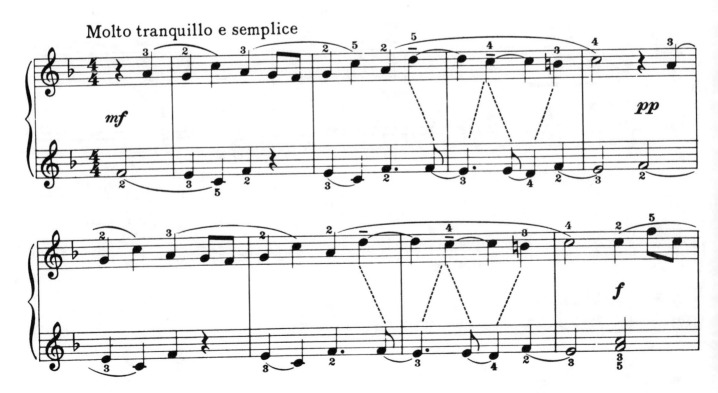

Molto tranquillo e semplice

Suggestion for supplementary solo in sheet form
HOE CAKE SHUFFLE by Charles Leslie makes an attractive encore piece to the above.

W.M.Co. 6602

SIX-EIGHT TIME

In six-eight time there are SIX counts to the bar and *a quaver gets one count*. There are TWO ACCENTS to the bar; the primary accent falling on the FIRST count and the secondary accent on the FOURTH count.

Time Values in six-eight time

♪ = One count

♩ = Two counts   ♩ = Four counts

♩. = Three counts   ♩. = Six counts

Little Tom Tinker

from
An Old Round

1st time bar

2nd time bar

Repeat by returning to the beginning.
Skip 1st time bar second time through.
Play 2nd time bar instead.

ALTERNATING HANDS

We're in the Army now,
The farmer's behind his plough,
We're learning to work
And scorning to shirk
We're peace-time soldiers now!

We'll plant our flowers gay,
And study, work and play.
Good neighbours we'll be
To friends o'er the sea
We're peace-time soldiers now!

Peace-Time Soldiers

Allegro moderato

W.M.Co. 6602

BROKEN CHORDS AS MELODY

The Airship

Up in the air midst fleecy clouds
And sharp winds, swinging high;
The airman lives like an eagle bold
Oh! but it's great to fly!

Allegretto

W.M.Co.6602

Seasonal Pleasure
at
CHRISTMAS TIME

Two Carols are here presented for use at Christmas time.   Since pupils vary in their rate of progress and begin their piano study at different times of the year it was obviously impossible to select the exact spot in the book to place the Carols so that they would coincide with the Christmas Season.

It is intended that, no matter what part of the book the pupil might be studying, these Carols be given as supplementary solos to be learned for the Christmas Concert Programme.

Good King Wenceslas

Old English Tune

We Three Kings of Orient Are

J. H. Hopkins

Printed in Great Britain by Printwise (Haverhill) Limited, Suffolk 11/03 (49491)

GLOSSARY OF TERMS, SIGNS
AND ABBREVIATIONS USED IN THIS BOOK

Signs or Abbreviations	Terms	Meaning
>	accent	To emphasize or stress a certain note or beat
	allegretto	Light and lively
	allegro	Fast
	andante	Slow
	andantino	Slow—but not as slow as *andante*
	animato	With animation
	arpeggio	In the style of a harp—broken chord
	a tempo	Resume original tempo
◁	crescendo	A gradual increase in the tone
D.C.	Da Capo	Return to beginning
D.C. al Fine	Da Capo al Fine	Return to beginning and play to *Fine*
▷	diminuendo	A gradual decrease in the tone
	espressivo	Expressively
Fine	Finale	The end
f	forte	Loud
ff	fortissimo	Very loud
	largo	Very slowly
	legato	Connected, bound together
mf	mezzo forte	Moderately loud
mp	mezzo piano	Moderately soft
	moderato	At a moderate tempo
	molto	Much
	Nocturne	Night Song
8va or 8	octave above	Play all notes under this sign one octave higher than written
⌢	pause	To hold or pause, according to taste
p	piano	Softly
pp	pianissimo	Very softly
	poco	Little
rit.	ritard	A gradual slowing of the tempo
𝅗𝅥̄	sostenuto	Sustained—with singing quality
𝅘𝅥̇	staccato	Detached
	tempo	Time—rate of speed

W.M.Co. 6602

Certificate of Merit

This certifies that

....

has successfully completed

GRADE 1

OF

JOHN THOMPSON'S
"MELODY ALL THE WAY"

and is eligible for promotion to

GRADE 1-PLUS

....

Teacher

Date...